I SAW A DINOSAUR

by John Foster

pictures by Diana Catchpole

I saw a dinosaur dressed in pyjamas,
Sitting on a roundabout, eating bananas.

LITTER

I saw a dinosaur dressed in a hat,
Playing tennis with a ginger cat.

I saw a dinosaur dressed in a skirt,
Riding a bicycle, splashing up dirt.

I saw a dinosaur dressed in a coat,
Whizzing down the river in a motorboat.

I saw a dinosaur dressed in jeans,
Sitting on a seesaw, eating baked beans.

I saw a dinosaur dressed in socks,
Playing snakes and ladders with a fox.

I saw a dinosaur with nothing on,
He shouted "Goodbye!", then he was gone.